Elizabeth

For the occ

your Grade IV piano

Exam

With lots of love

Dinah

G000269584

26 June 1985

THE MAESTRO

By the Author of

THE HOFFNUNG SYMPHONY ORCHESTRA
THE HOFFNUNG MUSIC FESTIVAL
THE HOFFNUNG COMPANION TO MUSIC
HOFFNUNG'S MUSICAL CHAIRS
HOFFNUNG'S ACOUSTICS

The Maestro

by

GERARD HOFFNUNG

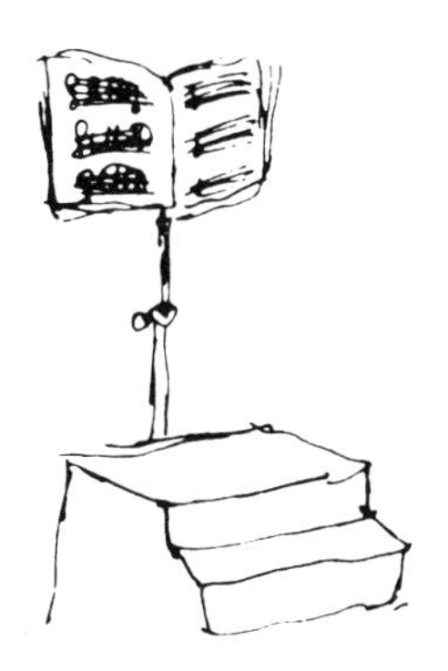

SOUVENIR PRESS

First published 1953 by Dennis Dobson

This edition first published 1983 by Souvenir Press Ltd, 43 Great Russell Street, London WC1B 3PA

Reprinted November 1983

ISBN 0 285 62617 5

Printed in Great Britain by
William Clowes Limited
Beccles and London

To
Annetta, my wife

Alerto

Introduzione

Interruzione

Preciso

Rallentando

Dolce

Affettuoso

Con amore

Con anima

Amoroso

Risoluto

Lusingando

Con delicatezza

Pizzicato

Scherzando

Giocoso

Scherzo

Giojoso

Allegro giocoso

Non troppo

Sotto voce

Piano

Pianissimo

Diminuendo

Molto diminuendo

Tacet

Pomposo

Molto pomposo

Subito piano

A cappella

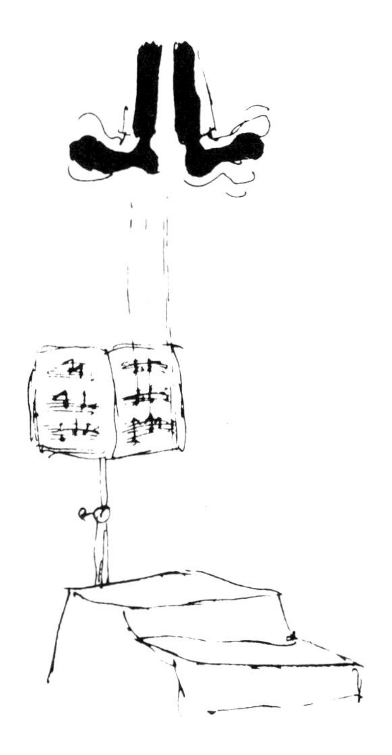

A cappella continuoso

Martellato

Tempo primo

Serioso

Mesto

Doloroso

Molto doloroso

Troppo doloroso

G.P.

Affrettando

Appassionato

Basso

Vigoroso

Con forza

Molto vigoroso

Attacca

Furioso

Rinforzando

Strepitoso

Fortissimo vivacissimo

Finale furioso

Bravo bravissimo